rockschool®

Female Vocals
Grade 5

*Performance pieces, technical exercises and in-depth guidance
for Rockschool examinations*

Acknowledgements

Published by Rockschool Ltd. © 2014 under license from Music Sales Ltd.
Catalogue Number RSK091405
ISBN: 978-1-908920-55-3

AUDIO
Backing tracks produced by Music Sales Limited
Supporting test backing tracks recorded by Jon Musgrave, Jon Bishop and Duncan Jordan
Supporting test vocals recorded by Duncan Jordan
Supporting tests mixed at Langlei Studios by Duncan Jordan
Mastered by Duncan Jordan

MUSICIANS
Neal Andrews, Lucie Burns (Lazy Hammock), Jodie Davies,Tenisha Edwards, Noam Lederman,
Beth Loates-Taylor, Dave Marks, Salena Mastroianni, Paul Miro, Ryan Moore, Jon Musgrave,
Chris Smart, Ross Stanley, T-Jay, Stacy Taylor, Daniel Walker

PUBLISHING
Compiled and edited by James Uings, Simon Troup, Stephen Lawson and Stuart Slater
Internal design and layout by Simon and Jennie Troup, Digital Music Art
Cover designed by Philip Millard, Philip Millard Design
Fact Files written by Stephen Lawson, Owen Bailey and Michael Leonard
Additional proofing by Chris Bird, Ronan Macdonald, Jonathan Preiss and Becky Baldwin
Cover photography © IBL / Rex Features
Full transcriptions by Music Sales Ltd.

SYLLABUS
Vocal specialists: Martin Hibbert and Eva Brandt
Additional Consultation: Emily Nash, Stuart Slater and Sarah Page
Supporting Tests Composition: Martin Hibbert, James Uings, Jon Musgrave, Jodie Davies,
Ryan Moore, Chris Hawkins, Jonathan Preiss

PRINTING
Printed and bound in the United Kingdom by Caligraving Ltd.
Media hosting by Dropcards

DISTRIBUTION
Exclusive Distributors: Music Sales Ltd.

CONTACTING ROCKSCHOOL
www.rockschool.co.uk
Telephone: +44 (0)845 460 4747
Fax: +44 (0)845 460 1960

Table of Contents

Introductions & Information

Page

2   Acknowledgements
3   Table of Contents
4   Welcome to Female Vocals Grade 5

Rockschool Grade Pieces

Page

5	'Mama Do'	Pixie Lott
13	'Set Fire To The Rain'	Adele
19	'Spotlight'	Jennifer Hudson
27	'Stay'	Rihanna
35	'Suddenly I See'	KT Tunstall
43	'Nutbush City Limits'	Tina Turner

Technical Exercises

Page

50   Scales, Arpeggios, Intervals, Melodic Study & Backing Vocals

Supporting Tests

Page

52   Sight Reading
53   Improvisation & Interpretation
54   Ear Tests
55   General Musicianship Questions

Additional Information

Page

56   Entering Exams, Exam Procedure & Marking Schemes
57   Improvisation Requirements & Free Choice Pieces

Welcome to Rockschool Female Vocals Grade 5

Welcome to the Rockschool Female Vocals Grade 5 pack. This book and accompanying download card contain everything you need to sing at this grade.

Vocals Exams

At each grade you have the option of taking one of two different types of examination:

- **Grade Exam:** a Grade Exam is a mixture of music performances, technical work and tests. You prepare three pieces (two of which may be Free Choice Pieces) and the contents of the Technical Exercise section. This accounts for 75% of the exam marks. The other 25% consists of: *either* a Sight Reading *or* an Improvisation & Interpretation test (10%), two Ear Tests (10%), and finally you will be asked five General Musicianship Questions (5%). The pass mark is 60%.

- **Performance Certificate:** in a Performance Certificate you sing five pieces. Up to three of these can be Free Choice Pieces. Each song is marked out of 20 and the pass mark is 60%.

Book Contents

The book is divided into a number of sections. These are:

- **Exam Pieces:** in this book you will find six well-known pieces of Grade 5 standard. Each song is preceded by a Fact File detailing information about the original recording, the artist who sang on it and some recommended listening if you wish to research the artist further.

- **Piano and guitar notation:** every exam piece is printed with a piano part and guitar chords. Both are a representation of the overall band arrangement. These have been included to assist you with your practice should you wish to use a piano and/or guitar for accompaniment. In your exam you must perform to the backing tracks provided.

- **Vocal score:** in addition to the piano/vocal/guitar arrangement there is also a separate vocal-only score to allow you to view the vocal part on a single sheet of paper.

- **Technical Exercises:** there are a range of technical exercises in this grade. Some are notated in full, and some give a range of starting notes.

- **Supporting Tests and General Musicianship Questions:** in Vocals Grade 5 there are three supporting tests – *either* a Sight Reading *or* an Improvisation & Interpretation test and two Ear Tests – and a set of General Musicianship Questions (GMQs) asked at the end of each exam. Examples of the types of tests likely to appear in the exam are printed in this book.

- **General Information:** finally, you will find information on exam procedures, including online examination entry, marking schemes, information on Free Choice Pieces and improvisation requirements for each grade.

Audio

Each song in Vocals Grade 5 has an audio track that can be downloaded via the download card that comes with the book. This is a backing track with the vocal taken off so you can sing along with the band. The backing tracks should be used in examinations. There are also audio examples of the supporting tests printed in the book.

The audio files are supplied in MP3 format, the most widely compatible audio format in common usage – MP3s will likely be familiar to anyone with a computer, iPod, smartphone or similar device. Once downloaded you will be able to play them on any compatible device; we hope that you find this extra versatility useful.

Download cards

Download cards are easy to use – simply go to *www.dropcards.com/rsvocals* and type in the code on the back of your card. It's best to do this somewhere with a good connection, to ensure that the download is uninterrupted. If you have any problems with your download, you should be able to resolve them at *www.dropcards.com/help*.

We hope you enjoy using this book. You can find further details about Rockschool's Vocals and other instrumental syllabuses on our website: *www.rockschool.co.uk*.

SONG TITLE: MAMA DO

ALBUM: TURN IT UP

RELEASED: 2009

LABEL: MERCURY

GENRE: POP

PERSONNEL: PIXIE LOTT (VOX)

MADS HAUGE (VARIOUS)

ANDERS KALLMARK (SYNTH)

PHIL THORNALLEY (PIANO)

UK CHART PEAK: 1

US CHART PEAK: N/A

BACKGROUND INFO

'Mama Do' was the lead single from Pixie Lott's debut album, *Turn It Up*.

THE BIGGER PICTURE

Victoria Louise Lott was born in London in 1991. Her mother called her Pixie because she was "such a tiny, cute baby who looked like a fairy". Lott began singing at an early age – though it was hymns at the church school she attended before she discovered pop via Whitney Houston and Mariah Carey. She would impersonate her musical heroes at family gatherings, where the encouragement of relatives led her mum to enrol Lott, aged 11, at the famous Italia Conti stage school. The school's musical theatre focus wasn't for Lott, who had been writing her own songs and had her sights firmly set on a career in pop. At 15, Pixie Lott was signed to Island Def Jam Music Group, until a change of managers led her to Mercury Records in the UK and Interscope Records in America. She signed a publishing deal with Sony/ATV Music Publishing in 2007 and has written for Alexandra Burke among others. Her debut album, *Turn It Up*, was released in 2009. Lott co-wrote 10 of its 12 tracks, including the Top 20 singles 'Boys And Girls', 'Cry Me Out' and title track 'Turn It Up'.

NOTES

'Mama Do' was written by two songwriters/ producers. Mads Hauge, a Norwegian, had previously written the single 'Soulmate' for Natasha Bedingfield and has also worked with Eliza Doolittle and Savage Garden frontman Darren Hayes. The other songwriter on 'Mama Do' was Englishman Phil Thornalley, a musical colleague of Hauge's who co-wrote Natalia Imbruglia's hit 'Torn'. Thornalley and Hauge often work together on tracks, with Thornalley producing and Hauge providing melodies and lyrics. "It's about sneaking out the house and going to see a specific person without your parents knowing about it," said Pixie, "It's a really cool song because it suits my age and I can relate to it. I mean, there have been a couple of occasions when I might have sneaked out the house and not told my mum and dad."

RECOMMENDED LISTENING

'Cry Me Out' has a similar soul/R'n'B vibe to 'Mama Do' and was written by Lott, Hauge, Thornalley and Colin Campsie for *Turn It Up*. 'Boys And Girls' was a Number 1 single from the same album, with more of a pop sheen reminiscent of Girls Aloud and Sugababes. 'All About Tonight' is a more uptempo track that brought Lott's sound up to date in 2011.

Mama Do

Pixie Lott

Words & Music by Phil Thornalley & Mads Hauge

oh.) if she knew 'bout me_____ and you?____

(Uh oh, uh oh.) What would my Dad——dy

say____ (Uh oh, uh oh.) if he saw me

hurt____ this way?____ Uh oh, uh oh.

SONG TITLE: SET FIRE TO THE RAIN
ALBUM: 21
RELEASED: 2010
LABEL: XL
GENRE: POP

PERSONNEL: ADELE (VOX)
FRASER T. SMITH (VARIOUS)

UK CHART PEAK: 11
US CHART PEAK: 1

BACKGROUND INFO

'Set Fire To The Rain' was the third single released from Adele's second album, *21*.

THE BIGGER PICTURE

Adele Laurie Blue Adkins was born in London in 1988. She began singing at the age of four and later became a fan of the Spice Girls, of whom she has said, "They made me what I am today." As a teenager, she attended the BRIT School and graduated in the same year as Leona Lewis and Jessie J. Like Jessie J, Adkins is herself an accomplished songwriter and wrote many of the songs on her debut album, *19*, which was released by XL Recordings in 2008. The album went to Number 1 in the UK and eventually went double platinum (selling more than two million copies) in America. Her second album, *21*, was co-written with various songwriters but rather than giving up control of her writing and recording process, Adkins seemed more and more to be calling the shots as she grew in confidence. For example, when Rick Rubin was employed to produce finished versions of demos that she had recorded previously, she rejected the new versions in favour of the demos. Fans of the singer often admire this personal strength as much as they do her considerable artistic merits.

NOTES

'Set Fire To The Rain' was co-written by Adele and songwriter/producer Fraser T. Smith, who once worked as Craig David's guitarist and co-wrote 'Broken Strings' by James Morrison. "When she walked into the session I already had a rolling drum beat going and some chords in my head," said Smith, "She delivered a great vocal and we bashed it out." The demo he and Adele recorded was so good, Smith was asked to produce the final version for the album *21* – and Adele's demo vocal was kept. Adele claims she came up with the idea for the song when her lighter stopped working in the rain. "It's about the contradictions in relationships," she said. "One person says this, one person says that. I was really heartbroken when I met who the song's about and he kind of brought me back to life and put me back together… and he was a ******** as well!"

RECOMMENDED LISTENING

'Chasing Pavements' and 'Make You Feel My Love' are good examples of Adele's vocal talent, but it was later singles 'Rolling In The Deep', 'Someone Like You' and 'Skyfall' that showed how much the singer had grown in such a short space of time – between the ages of 19 and 21, in fact.

Set Fire To The Rain

Adele

Words & Music by Fraser Smith & Adele Adkins

SONG TITLE: SPOTLIGHT
ALBUM: JENNIFER HUDSON
RELEASED: 2008
LABEL: ARISTA
GENRE: R'N'B

PERSONNEL: JENNIFER HUDSON (VOX)

UK CHART PEAK: 11
US CHART PEAK: 24

BACKGROUND INFO

'Spotlight' was the first single from Jennifer Hudson's self-titled debut album.

THE BIGGER PICTURE

Jennifer Kate Hudson was born in 1981 in Chicago. She began singing at the age of seven, performing in her church choir. As a teenager, Hudson worked at Burger King until she got a job on a Disney cruise ship, playing the muse Calliope in *Hercules – A Muse-ical Comedy*. At that time, she had ambitions to compete in the TV singing contest *American Idol*: "I said, 'If I can get through the ship, that means I'm cut out for *Idol*.'" In 2003 Hudson auditioned successfully for the third season of *American Idol*, judge Randy Jackson describing her cover of Aretha Franklin's 'Share Your Love With Me' as "brilliant". However, the singer only made it as far as the final seven, despite being considered one of the strongest singers. Hudson's fortunes changed the following year, when she starred in the musical *Dreamgirls* with Beyoncé. Her performance in the film won several awards, including a Golden Globe for Best Actress in a Supporting Role. She was signed to Arista Records in 2006 and released her debut album in 2008.

NOTES

'Spotlight' was written for Jennifer Hudson by platinum-selling recording artist Ne-Yo and Norwegian songwriting/production duo Stargate (Tor Erik Hermansen and Mikkel S. Eriksen). Ne-Yo, Hermansen and Eriksen regularly work together. Two of their most successful collaborations are 'Unfaithful' by Rihanna and 'Irreplaceable' by Beyoncé. As a duo, Stargate wrote 'Don't Stop The Music' (Rihanna), 'Firework' (Katy Perry) and 'Beautiful Liar' (Beyoncé & Shakira). Ne-Yo met Hermansen and Eriksen in Sony Music Studios, New York, while he was working on material for his debut album, *In My Own Words*. The three hit it off and began their musical relationship by writing 'So Sick' for *In My Own Words*. It was released as the second single from the album and went to Number 1 in America and the UK.

RECOMMENDED LISTENING

Jennifer Hudson's performance of 'And I Am Telling You I Am Not Going' from the film *Dreamgirls* drew comparisons with Barbara Streisand, Bette Midler and Aretha Franklin. 'Think Like A Man' puts the singer in a more contemporary R'n'B setting – where she sounds equally at home.

Spotlight

Jennifer Hudson

Words & Music by Mikkel Eriksen, Tor Erik Hermansen & Shaffer Smith

SONG TITLE: STAY
ALBUM: UNAPOLOGETIC
RELEASED: 2013
LABEL: DEF JAM
GENRE: POP

PERSONNEL: RIHANNA (VOX)
MIKKY EKKO (VOX)

UK CHART PEAK: 4
US CHART PEAK: 3

BACKGROUND INFO

'Stay' was the second single released from Rihanna's seventh studio album, *Unapologetic*.

THE BIGGER PICTURE

Robin Rihanna Fenty was born in 1988 in Barbados. She grew up listening to reggae and started singing around the age of seven. In her early teens, Fenty formed a girl group with two classmates. The trio caught the attention of holidaying songwriter/producer Evan Rogers (who had worked previously with N Sync, Boyzone and Christina Aguilera) in 2004. The group was invited to audition for Rogers, who said: "The minute Rihanna walked into the room, it was like the other two girls didn't exist." For a year, Fenty travelled back and forth between Barbados and Rogers's home in Connecticut, USA, where the experienced Rogers mentored the fledgling performer. When Fenty turned 16, she relocated to America and moved in with Rogers and his wife. By 2005, she had a four-song demo, which Rogers shopped to record companies, quickly landing Fenty a contract with Def Jam. By August, Def Jam had released her debut album, *Music Of The Sun* – the start of a recording career that's made Rihanna the most successful female singer of her generation.

NOTES

'Stay' was co-written by guest vocalist Mikky Ekko and Justin Parker. Ekko is a singer-songwriter signed to RCA Records. Besides releasing his own albums, Ekko has worked with various other recording artists, including David Guetta (on the song 'One Voice'). Justin Parker is an English singer-songwriter who has written for Lana Del Rey, Bat For Lashes and Ellie Goulding. Ekko says he was "freaked out" when he found out 'Stay' was going to be recorded by Rihanna, as it has such a personal meaning to him. However, he came round to the idea when he met Rihanna and heard the vocal she had recorded: "The track had become so special to me as well," Ekko said, "and knowing what the track means to me and what I think it means to her too, it really worked. It speaks to such an intimate side of her that is so rare and so far removed from what people think of her."

RECOMMENDED LISTENING

'Pon De Replay' was Rihanna's first single and one of four tracks on the demo that got her signed to Def Jam. Since then, the singer has had an endless stream of hit singles. Some of the best – 'Umbrella', 'Take A Bow' and 'Don't Stop The Music' – feature on her first Number 1 album *Good Girl Gone Bad* (2007).

Stay

Rihanna
Words & Music by Justin Parker & Mikky Ekko

just some-thing you take, it's gi-ven.

And I want you to stay.

Oh_____ the rea-son I_____ hold_____ on._____

Oh_____ 'cause I need this hole gone._____

SONG TITLE: SUDDENLY I SEE
ALBUM: EYE TO THE TELESCOPE
RELEASED: 2005
LABEL: RELENTLESS RECORDS
GENRE: POP

PERSONNEL: KT TUNSTALL (VOX+GTR)

UK CHART PEAK: 12
US CHART PEAK: 21

BACKGROUND INFO

'Suddenly I See' was the third single from KT Tunstall's debut album, *Eye To The Telescope*.

THE BIGGER PICTURE

Kate Victoria Tunstall was born in 1975. She was adopted as a baby and grew up with her adoptive family in St. Andrews, Scotland. At 15, she started writing songs and spent her early teens learning to play guitar, piano and flute. She formed her first band, The Happy Campers, while taking a scholarship at a school in Connecticut, USA. KT (she dropped 'Kate' because it sounded like "a farmer's daughter") then studied music at Royal Holloway University, London, where she and a mandolin player won a battle of the bands. After university, she spent six years unemployed back in Scotland, performing and writing songs with the ambition of having an album out by the age of 30. Thanks to the offer of a contract with Relentless Records, which she initially rejected, Tunstall achieved her goal, releasing her debut album, *Eye To The Telescope*, in 2004. "It was real luck," she said. "My album came out in December and I turned 30 in June." She came to the nation's attention in the UK after replacing rapper Nas with 24 hours' notice on the TV show *Later… With Jools Holland*.

NOTES

'Suddenly I See' was inspired by the American singer-songwriter and poet Patti Smith. KT wrote the lyrics about the famous black and white photograph of Smith on the cover of her album *Horses*. The song was featured in the film *The Devil Wears Prada*, which helped it to Number 21 in the American singles chart (KT's only other single to chart in the States was 'Black Horse & The Cherry Tree', which went to Number 20). Tunstall was surprised by the success of her song – inspired by the 'godmother of punk' and a *Commandeur* of France's cultural institution, the *Ordre Des Arts Et Des Lettres* – in the context of a film about a woman in thrall to the fashion industry. "I didn't realise the lyrics could perfectly fit a chick flick," she said, "and it could sound like I was singing about wanting to be a f***ing model!"

RECOMMENDED LISTENING

'Black Horse & The Cherry Tree' was the song KT Tunstall performed on *Later… With Jools Holland*, a performance that's often cited as her breakthrough. It's worth finding online to see how Tunstall skilfully uses a looper pedal to provide all her backing. 'Other Side Of The World' is an affecting ballad from the same album, her debut, *Eye To The Telescope*.

Suddenly I See

KT Tunstall
Words & Music by KT Tunstall

SONG TITLE: NUTBUSH CITY LIMITS
ALBUM: NUTBUSH CITY LIMITS
RELEASED: 1973
LABEL: UNITED ARTISTS
GENRE: FUNK ROCK

PERSONNEL: TINA TURNER (VOX)
JAMES LEWIS (GUITAR)

UK CHART PEAK: 4
US CHART PEAK: 22

BACKGROUND INFO

'Nutbush City Limits' was the lead single from Ike & Tina Turner's 1973 album of the same name.

THE BIGGER PICTURE

Tina Turner was born Anna Mae Bullock in 1939 in Nutbush, Tennessee. As a child, Bullock sang in the choir at her local Baptist church, but showed no interest in a career in music through her childhood and teenage years. Her break came in 1958 when she and her sister went to a nightclub in Detroit to watch Ike Turner and his band the Kings Of Rhythm. The group would often invite female members of the audience onstage to sing a song with them, and that night a microphone was thrust in front of Anna Mae's face. Turner and his bandmates were so impressed that they asked Anna Mae to stay onstage and perform some more. She joined the band, changed her name to Tina and, under the tutelage of Ike, began recording. Her first single was 'Box Top', on which she appeared as 'Little Ann'. She later married Ike and took his name. Their troubled relationship was the subject of the film *What's Love Got To Do With It*. The couple divorced in 1976. Since then, Tina (who kept her stage name) has built a solo career so successful it eclipses her time with Ike.

NOTES

Tina Turner wrote the lyrics for 'Nutbush City Limits' as a tribute to her home of Nutbush, Tennessee. Nutbush isn't actually a city – more a rural area inhabited by a couple of hundred people. As such, there are no city limits; clearly Tina Turner was using poetic licence here. However, it does have signs around its boundaries marked 'Nutbush Unincorporated', which wouldn't have made for quite so catchy a title. Tina Turner has recorded the song several times. This article refers to the original recording. It was rumoured for years that Marc Bolan of T. Rex played guitar on this version. However, this idea was scotched in a 2008 interview with Kings Of Rhythm guitarist James 'Bino' Lewis, who revealed himself to be the guitar player on the record.

RECOMMENDED LISTENING

From her days as one half of Ike & Tina Turner, 'Proud Mary' (a rip-roaring cover of a Creedence Clearwater Revival song) and 'River Deep, Mountain High' are just two highlights. Turner's most successful work as a solo artist leant more towards pop than funk and R&B. Tracks like 'What's Love Got To Do With It', 'The Best' and 'I Don't Wanna Lose You' are good examples of this later period of her career.

Nutbush City Limits

Tina Turner

Words & Music by Tina Turner

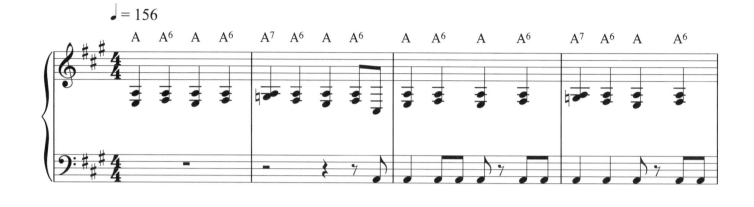

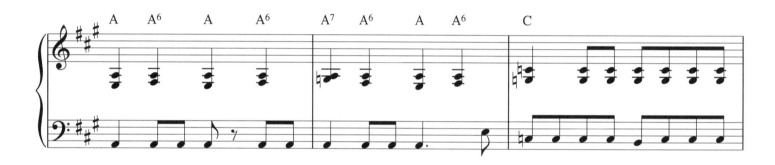

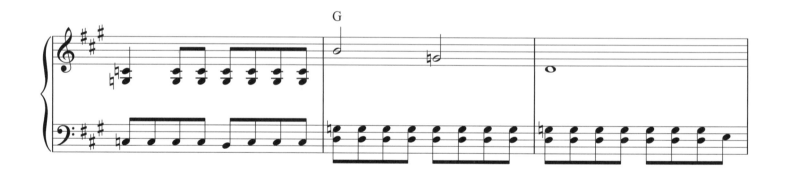

Nut - bush ci - ty,   Nut - bush ci - ty li - mits.

Lit - tle old__ town   in Ten - es - see,   it's called

a quiet   lit - tle old com - mun - i - ty.   A

Repeat ad lib. to fade

Verse 3:
You go to the fields on weekdays
And have a picnic on Labour Day
You go to town on Saturdays
And go to church on Sunday.

They call it Nutbush *etc.*

Verse 4:
No whiskey for sale
If you get drunk no bail
Salt pork and molasses
Is all you get in jail.

They call it Nutbush *etc,*

Fade out:
A one horse town
You have to watch
What you're putting down
In old Nutbush, oh Nutbush.

Technical Exercises

Group A: Scales

The minor pentatonic scale should be prepared as shown below. You may select any starting note from A–E. You will be asked if you would like to sing along to a metronome click or hear four clicks before you start. Whichever option you choose, you will hear your chosen starting note before the count starts. You may perform this test using any vocal sound except humming or whistling. The tempo is ♩=80.

Group B: Arpeggios

In this group, the arpeggio exercise needs to be prepared as shown below.

This test is performed to a metronome click track and you may select any starting note from A–E. You will hear the root note played on piano followed by a one-bar (three click) count-in. You may perform this test using any vocal sound except humming or whistling. The tempo is ♩=80.

A major arpeggio (ascending) and E⁷ arpeggio (descending)

Group C: Intervals

In this group, both the minor 6th and minor 7th intervals need to be prepared as below. You will be asked to perform one of them in the exam, as chosen by the examiner.

The examiner will choose a starting note within the range A–C. You will hear this note followed by a four-beat count-in. You may perform this test using any vocal sound except humming or whistling. The tempo is ♩=90.

Minor 6th interval

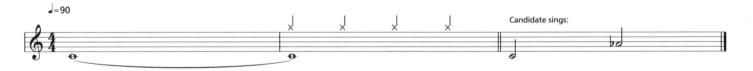

Minor 7th interval

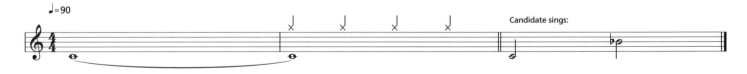

Group D: Melodic Study

In this group, the melodic test must be prepared as shown below. The test starts with a root note followed by a four-beat count. The test should be performed to the appropriate backing track which can be found on the download card.

Melismas and Scoops

Group E: Backing Vocals

In this group, both backing vocal parts need to be prepared as shown below. You will be asked to perform one of them in the exam, as chosen by the examiner. The chosen part must be sung alongside the other part on the recording. The backing tracks for these can be found on the download card.

Sight Reading

In this section you have a choice between:

- *Either* – a sight reading test
- *Or* – an improvisation and interpretation test (see facing page).

The examiner will ask you which one you wish to choose before commencing. Once you have decided, you cannot change your mind.

You will be given an eight-bar melody in the key of either D major, B♭ major, B minor or D minor. It will feature lyrics and cover a range of up to an octave. At this grade there is an element of improvisation. Bars 5 and 6 are a repeat of bars 1 and 2, and you need to improvise a melody in the final two bars. You will be given 90 seconds to practise, after which you will perform the test. The tempo is ♩=85–95.

During the practice time, you will be given the choice of a metronome click throughout or a count-in of four beats at the beginning. Whichever option you choose, the practice time will start with the examiner playing the root note. You will receive the same choice when performing the test. The test will start with the root note.

You may perform the improvised bars in this test using any vocal sound except humming or whistling.

Please note: the test shown is an example. The examiner will give you a different version in the exam.

Improvisation & Interpretation

The examiner will give you a chord sequence in the key of either D major, B♭ major, E minor or D minor. You must improvise a melody over the backing track. At this grade, there is also an element of sight reading, consisting of a two-bar section featuring lyrics, at the beginning of the test. You will be given 30 seconds to practise, after which the examiner will play the backing track twice. The first time is for you to rehearse and the second time is for you to perform the final version for the exam. The backing track will begin with a root note and a four-beat count-in on both playthroughs. The backing track is continuous, so once the first playthrough has finished, the root note and count-in of the second playthrough will start immediately. The tempo is ♩=90–100.

During the practice time, you will be given the choice of a metronome click throughout or a count-in of four beats at the beginning. Whichever option you choose, the practice time will start with the examiner playing the root note.

Please note: the test shown is an example. The examiner will give you a different version in the exam.

Ear Tests

In this section, there are two ear tests:

- Melodic Recall
- Harmony Vocals

You will find one example of each type of test printed below and you will be given both of them in the exam.

Test 1 | Melodic Recall

The examiner will play you a two-bar melody played to a drum backing. It will use the B♭ major or A natural minor scale (the examiner will decide which) and the first note will be the root note. You will hear the test twice. Each time the test is played, it starts with the root note and a four-beat count-in. There will be a short gap for you to practise after each playthrough. Next, you will hear a *vocal* count-in, after which you should sing the melody to the drum backing. The tempo is ♩=90.

It is acceptable to sing over the track as it is being played as well as practising after the first two playthroughs. The length of time available after the second playthrough is pre-recorded on the audio track, so the vocal count-in may begin while you are still practising.

You may perform this test using any vocal sound except humming or whistling.

Please note: the test shown is an example. The examiner will give you a different version in the exam.

Test 2 | Harmony Vocals

The examiner will play you a four-bar melody in the key of either A major or F major based on the I–IV–V chords. The recorded vocal part will sing the root or 3rd of each chord and you need to harmonise a diatonic third above this part using the same rhythm. The examiner will give you the lyrics.

You will hear the test twice. Each time the test is played, it starts with the root note and a four-beat count-in. There will be a short gap for you to practise after each playthrough. Next, you will hear a *vocal* count-in, after which you should perform the harmony line. The tempo is ♩=90–110.

It is acceptable to sing over the track as it is being played as well as practising after the first two playthroughs. The length of time available after the second playthrough is pre-recorded on the audio track, so the vocal count-in may begin while you are still practising.

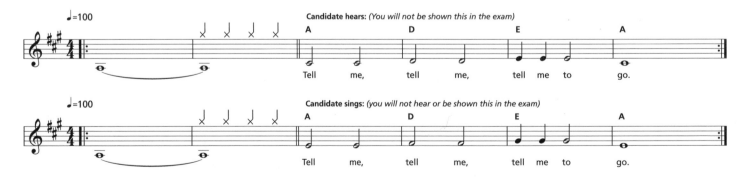

Please note: the test shown is an example. The examiner will give you a different version in the exam.

General Musicianship Questions

In this part of the exam you will be asked five questions. Four of these will be about general music knowledge and the fifth will be about your voice or the microphone.

Part 1 | General Music Knowledge

The examiner will ask four music knowledge questions from the categories below. The questions will be based on one of the pieces (including Free Choice Pieces) as performed by you in the exam. You can choose which one.

If there are handwritten notes on the piece you have chosen, the examiner may ask you to choose an alternative.

You will be asked to *identify:*
- Any pitch name. (You will need to state an appropriate flat, sharp or natural.)
- Whole-, half-, quarter-, eighth-, triplet eighth- and 16th-note values, and adjacent note value combinations.
- Whole-, half-, quarter-, eighth- and 16th-note rests, and adjacent rest combinations.
- Recognition of any interval up to an octave between two adjacent notes. (You will not need to state major, minor or perfect.)

You will be asked to *identify and explain:*
- The meaning of any time signature.
- The meaning of '*ad lib*'.
- The meaning of any dynamic marking.
- The meaning of the tempo marking.
- The meaning of the key signature. (State either major or relative minor.)
- The meaning of the swung rhythm marking.

Part 2 | Your Voice And The Microphone

The examiner will also ask you one question about your voice or the microphone. They will decide which. Brief demonstrations to assist your answer are acceptable.

You will be asked:
- Using your articulators (mouth/lips/tongue/teeth/jaw), how can you modify a bright 'ee' sound to produce a less bright tone?
- How would you prevent straining during prolonged use of louder dynamics?
- Suggest two exercises that can help develop control over dynamics across your range.
- Explain how you would use microphone technique to be able to sing at different volumes.

Entering Exams, Exam Procedure & Marking Schemes

Entering Exams
Entering a Rockschool exam is easy. You can enter online at *www.rockschool.co.uk* or by downloading and filling in an exam entry form. The full Rockschool examination terms and conditions as well as exam periods and current fees are available from our website or by calling +44 (0)845 460 4747.

Exam procedure
In the exam you can decide whether to start with the Performance Pieces or the Technical Exercises. These will be followed by the Supporting Tests (Ear Tests and Quick Study Pieces) and General Musicianship Questions.

Use Of Microphone
At Level 1 (Grades 1–3) microphone use is optional, although candidates may use one if they feel it will enhance their performance. At Level 2 (Grades 4–5) microphone use is obligatory for all pieces and at Level 3 (Grades 6–8) for the whole exam.

Marking Schemes
Below are the marking schemes for the two different types of Rockschool exam.

GRADE EXAMS | GRADES 1–5

ELEMENT	PASS	MERIT	DISTINCTION
Performance Piece 1	12–14 out of 20	15–17 out of 20	18+ out of 20
Performance Piece 2	12–14 out of 20	15–17 out of 20	18+ out of 20
Performance Piece 3	12–14 out of 20	15–17 out of 20	18+ out of 20
Technical Exercises	9–10 out of 15	11–12 out of 15	13+ out of 15
Either Sight Reading *or* Improvisation & Interpretation	6 out of 10	7–8 out of 10	9+ out of 10
Ear Tests	6 out of 10	7–8 out of 10	9+ out of 10
General Musicianship Questions	3 out of 5	4 out of 5	5 out of 5
TOTAL MARKS	60%+	74%+	90%+

PERFORMANCE CERTIFICATES | GRADES 1–8

ELEMENT	PASS	MERIT	DISTINCTION
Performance Piece 1	12–14 out of 20	15–17 out of 20	18+ out of 20
Performance Piece 2	12–14 out of 20	15–17 out of 20	18+ out of 20
Performance Piece 3	12–14 out of 20	15–17 out of 20	18+ out of 20
Performance Piece 4	12–14 out of 20	15–17 out of 20	18+ out of 20
Performance Piece 5	12–14 out of 20	15–17 out of 20	18+ out of 20
TOTAL MARKS	60%+	75%+	90%+

Improvisation Requirements & Free Choice Pieces

At Rockschool it is our aim to encourage creativity and individualism. We therefore give candidates the opportunity to express themselves musically within styles of their own choice. For this reason, Free Choice Pieces are accepted in all Vocals grades. In addition, all songs performed in exams from Grade 3 onwards have compulsory improvisation requirements.

Improvisation Requirements

From Grade 3, all songs, whether from the grade book or chosen as FCPs, need to incorporate improvisation. The improvisation can be prepared in advance, but is expected to be individually constructed, and needs to include **both** vocal ad-libbing and re-working of existing melody lines as follows:

Level 1 Grade 3:	Vocal ad-libbing (2–4 bars) and re-working of melody line (4 bars)
Level 2 Grades 4–5:	Vocal ad-libbing (4–8 bars) and re-working of melody line (4–8 bars)
Level 3 Grades 6–7:	Vocal ad-libbing (8–12 bars) and re-working of melody line (8 bars)
Level 3 Grades 8:	Vocal ad-libbing (12–16 bars) and re-working of melody line (8 bars)

For all pieces, you will need to highlight the sheet music to show the examiner the location of both ad-libbed and re-worked parts at the beginning of the exam.

Notes

- You are free to choose where you improvise. However, in all cases, improvisations need to be a continuous number of bars, not a number of smaller bars which in total add up to the ranges shown.

- Vocal ad-lib could be demonstrated in, for example, introductions, endings or open instrumental parts.

- Re-working of a melody could be demonstrated by altering any existing singing parts; for example, verses, choruses, bridges.

- For both ad-lib and re-working of a melody, you need to demonstrate an awareness of harmony, melody, phrasing, use of rhythms and incorporation of any appropriate expression in a stylistically appropriate manner. Range and content will be expected to increase progressively as you move through the grades.

- We would encourage re-working to take place later in a piece after the original has been presented to show you can portray the original, then you are able to adapt appropriately with individual colour.

- Improvisation can be a good place to demonstrate your head voice, which can often be omitted, reducing the technical content of a piece at a particular grade.

Free Choice Pieces (FCPs)

An FCP is defined as any piece outside the grade book, and can fall into two categories:

1) **Wider Repertoire:** a full list of pre-approved and regularly updated pieces can be found on *www.rockschool.co.uk*. These songs can be used *without* prior approval from Rockschool.

2) **Own Choice:** candidates can choose any song in any genre outside the grade book and wider repertoire. These songs can, however, only be used *with* prior approval from Rockschool. This requirement is compulsory and you need to contact the office to have your chosen piece(s) approved. Please allow five weeks before your exam to receive a decision.

We cannot accept any songs which have not been approved or are not contained in the grade book or wider repertoire.

For all grades, candidates can choose the following number of FCPs in the exam:

Grade Examinations:	Up to 2 of 3 pieces can be free choice. (At least one piece must be from the grade book.)
Performance Certificates:	Up to 3 of 5 pieces can be free choice. (At least two pieces must be from the grade book.)

For all FCPs, candidates will need to bring the sheet music and a backing track (without vocal part) on the day. A memory stick, iPod or CD/DVD is acceptable and we would also suggest a second source to be safe. It will not be necessary to bring the sheet music or backing tracks for pieces chosen from the grade book.

Copyright Information

Mama Do
(Thornalley/Hauge)
Universal Music Publishing MGB Limited

Set Fire To The Rain
(Smith/Adkins)
Chrysalis Music Limited/Universal Music Publishing Limited

Spotlight
(Eriksen/Hermansen/Smith)
Sony/ATV Music Publishing (UK) Limited/EMI Music Publishing Limited/Imagem Music

Stay
(Parker/Ekko)
Sony/ATV Music Publishing (UK) Limited

Suddenly I See
(Tunstall)
Sony/ATV Music Publishing (UK) Limited

Nutbush City Limits
(Turner)
EMI United Partnership Limited

mcps